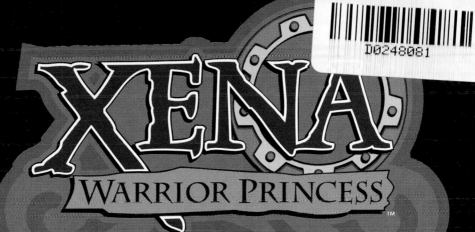

XENA
WARRIOR PRINCESS™

BLOOD AND SHADOWS

story
JOHN WAGNER

pencils
DAVIDÉ FABBRI

inks
MARK HEIKE

lettering
STEVE DUTRO

colors
DAVE McCAIG

title art
JASON PEARSON

DARK HORSE COMICS®

XENA: WARRIOR PRINCESS™– BLOOD AND SHADOWS

This volume collects issues seven through ten of the Dark horse comic-book series XENA: WARRIOR PRINCESS

publisher
MIKE RICHARDSON

series editor
DAVE LAND

collection editor
CHRIS WARNER

collection designer
LIA RIBACCHI

Special thanks to DEBBIE BRUNNER at STUDIOS USA and ALI RASUL at RENAISSANCE PICTURES

Published by
Dark horse Comics, Inc.
10956 SE Main Street
Milwaukie, OR 97222

www.darkhorse.com

To find a comics shop in your area, call the Comic Shop Locator Service toll free at 1-888-266-4226

First edition: January 2001
ISBN: 1-56971-521-1

10 9 8 7 6 5 4 3 2 1
Printed in Canada

CRAK

UNHH!

DROPPING *OUT,* PALIO?

N-NO!

AAHHH!

CHARIOTEER'S IN TROUBLE!

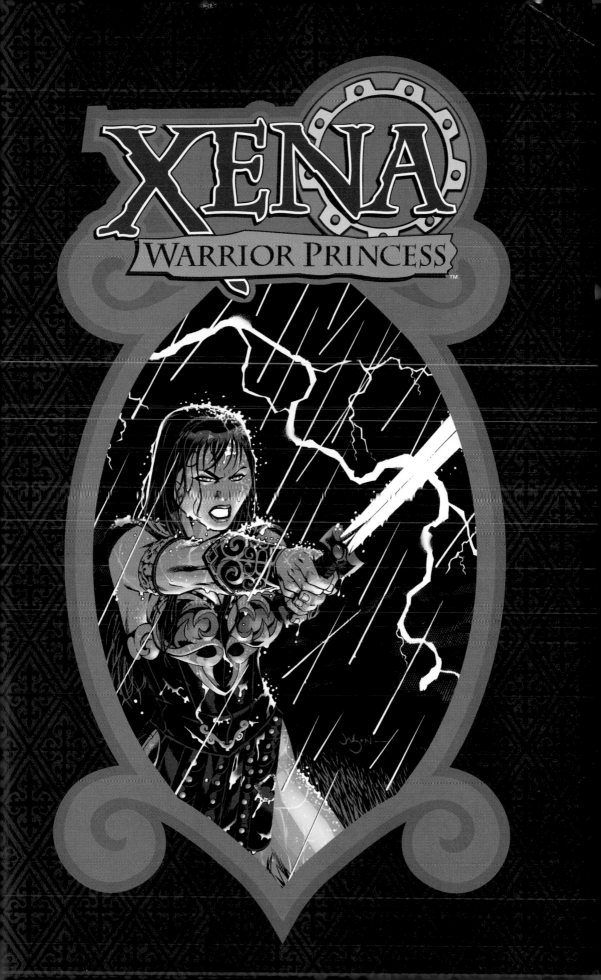

If You Go Down To The Woods

story
Ian Edginton

pencils
Mike Deodato, Jr.

inks
Neil Nelson

lettering
Steve Dutro

colors
Dave McCaig

title art
Jason Pearson

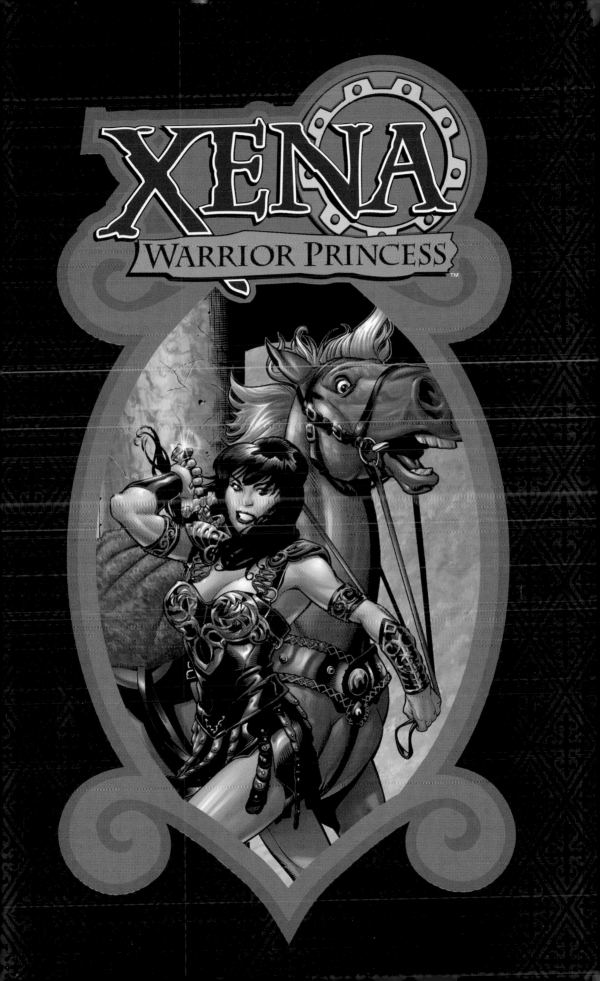

The Magnificent Sven

story
Ian Edginton

pencils
Mike Deodato, Jr.

inks
Neil Nelson

lettering
Steve Dutro

colors
Colorgraphix Production

title art
Terry Dodson
and Rachel Dodson

14